Leela s Tree

Written by Claire Llewellyn

Illustrated by Priscilla Lamont

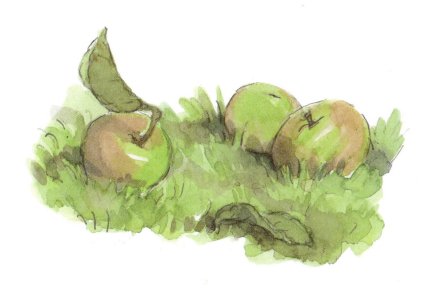

Leela has a tree.

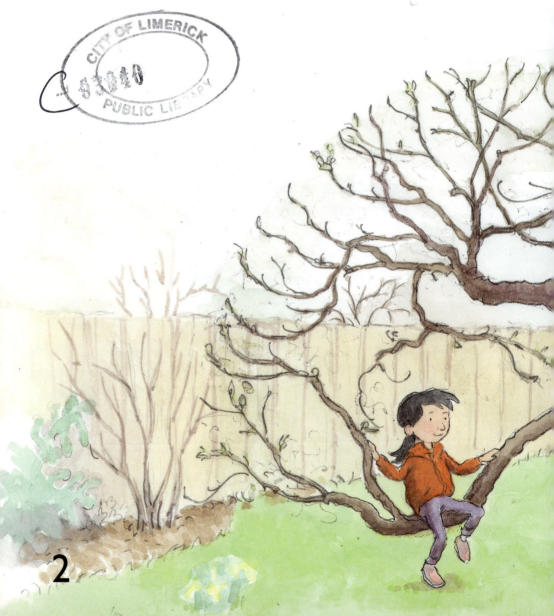

2

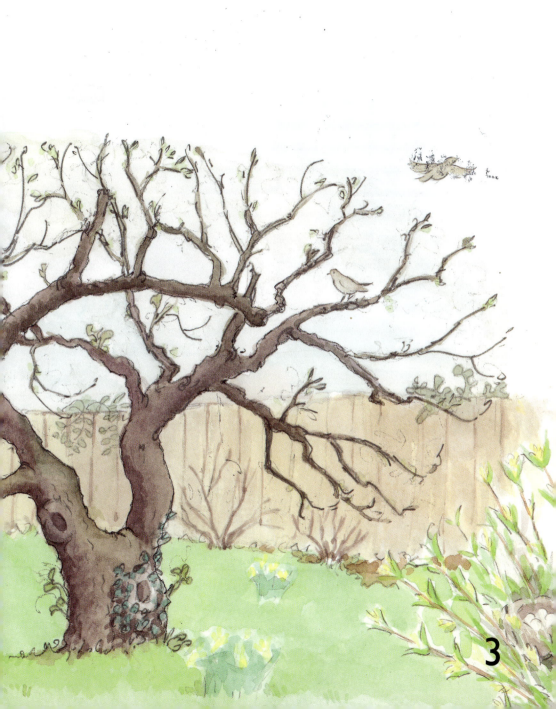

3

The tree has flowers.

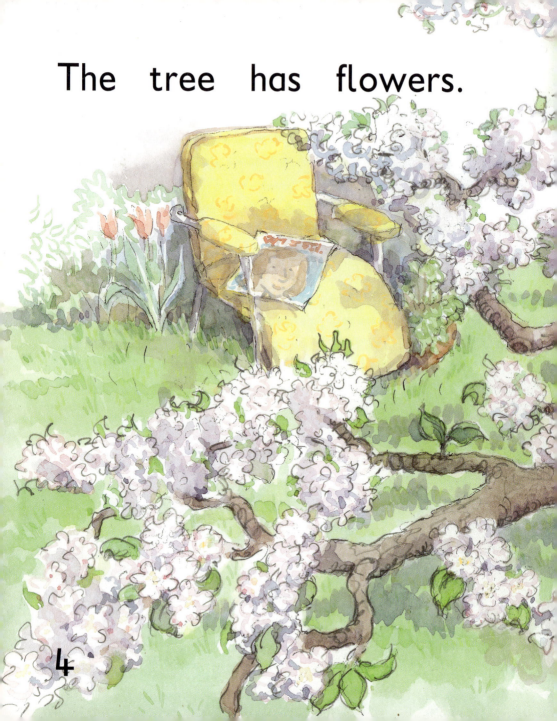

4

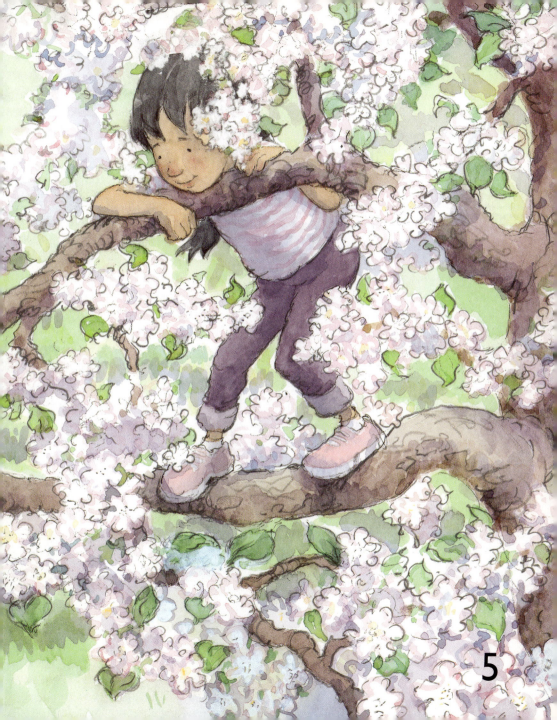

The tree has apples.

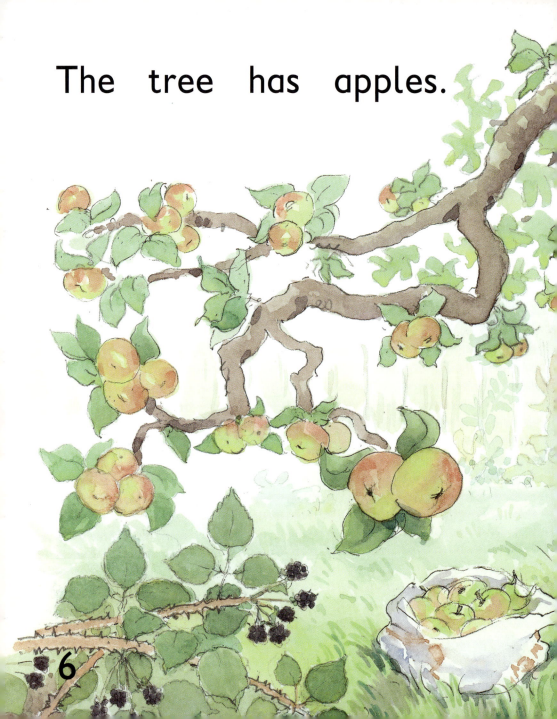

6

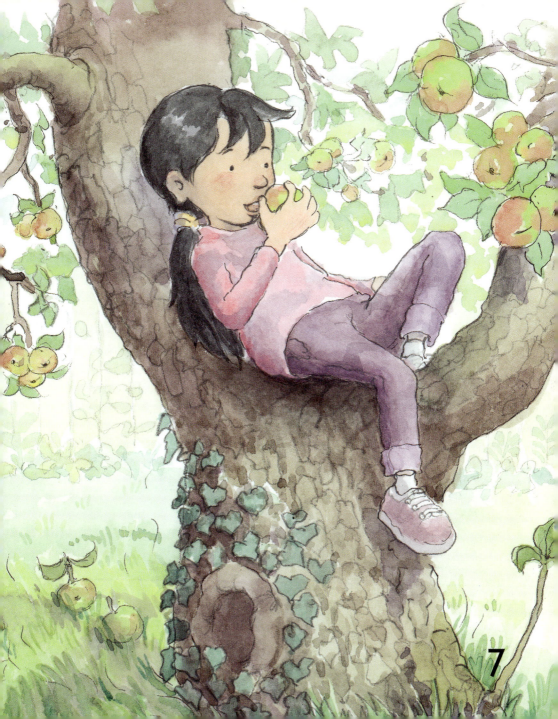

7

The tree has
a swing.

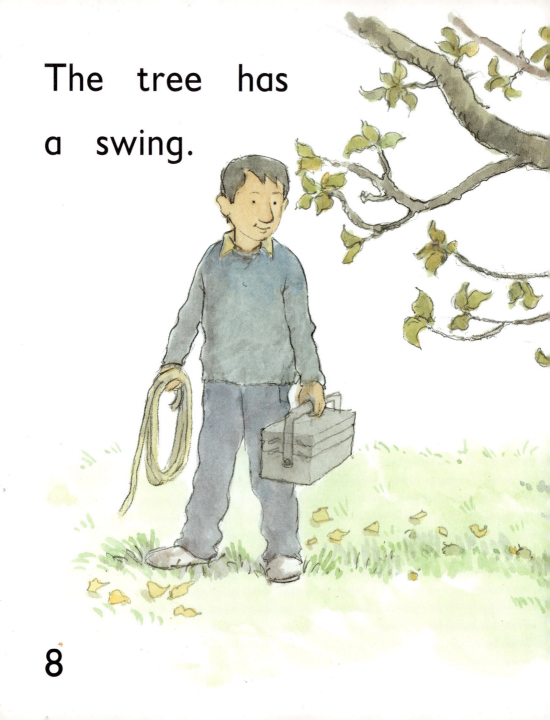

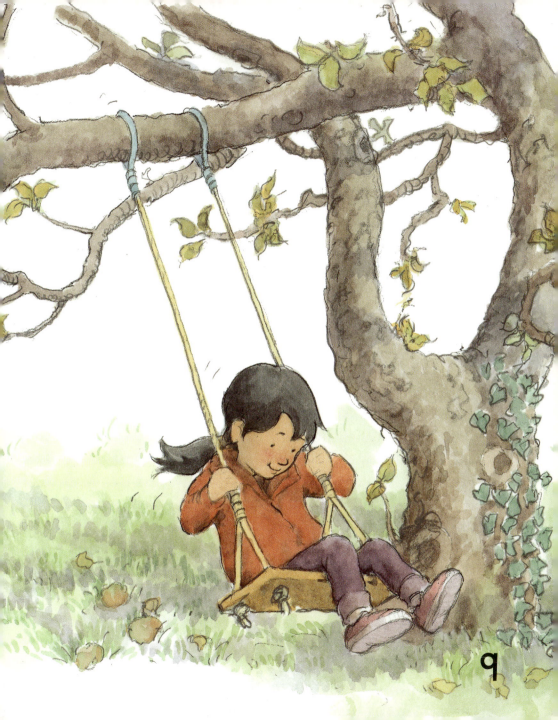

9

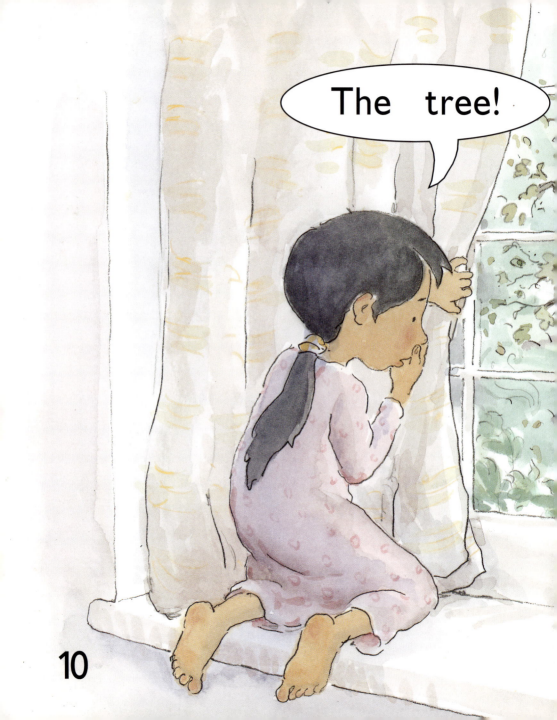

10

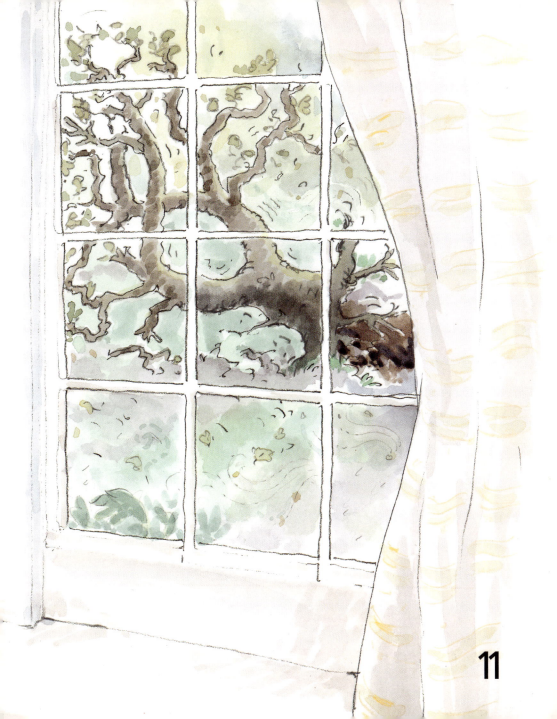

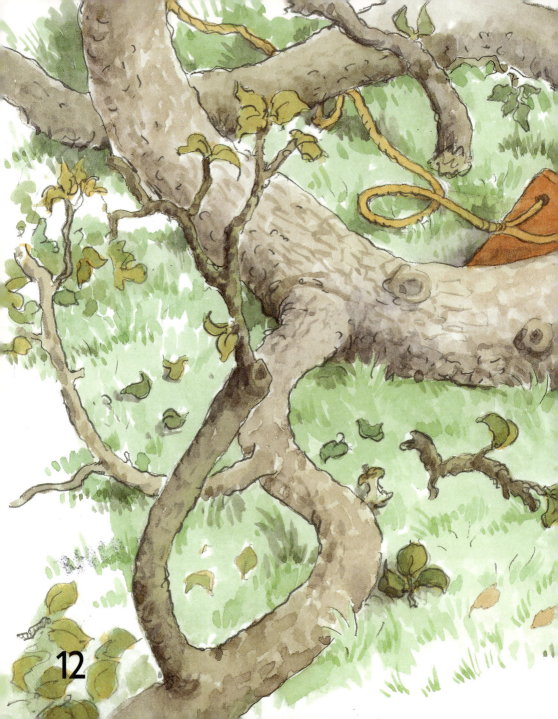

12

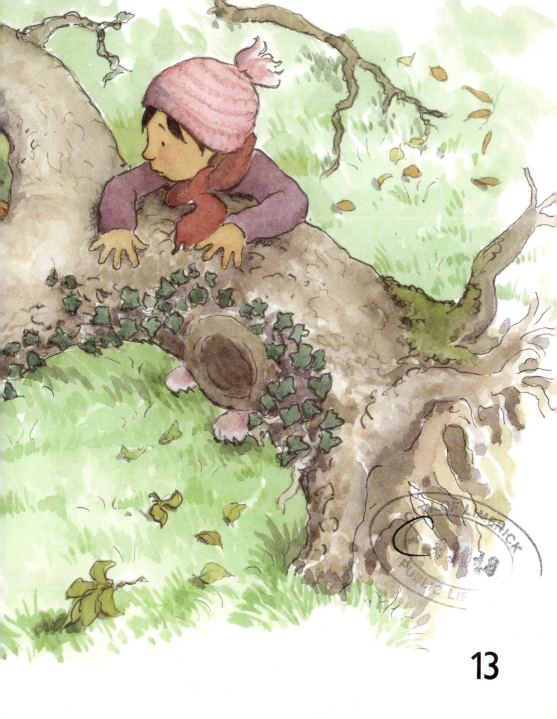

13

Leela has a new tree.

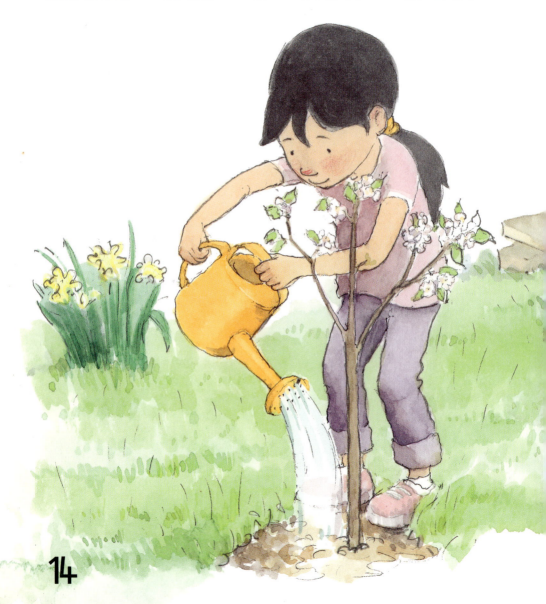

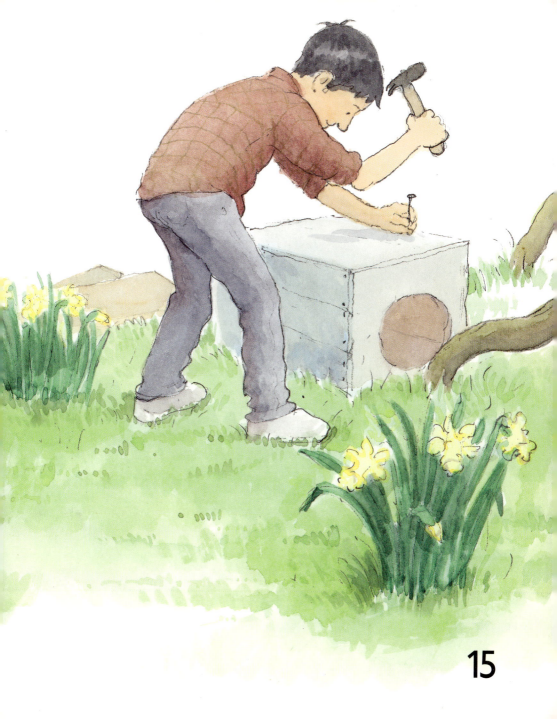

Leela has the old tree, too.